This Little Tiger book belongs to:

_____

_____

_____

For Jo – NL
For Daniel – TW

LITTLE TIGER PRESS
1 The Coda Centre
189 Munster Road, London SW6 6AW
www.littletiger.co.uk

First published in Great Britain 2010
This edition published 2016
Text copyright © Norbert Landa 2010
Illustrations copyright © Tim Warnes 2010
Visit Tim Warnes at www.ChapmanandWarnes.com
Norbert Landa and Tim Warnes have asserted their rights
to be identified as the author and illustrator of this work
under the Copyright, Designs and Patents Act, 1988

ISBN 978-1-84869-530-6
Printed in China

10 9 8 7 6 5 4 3 2 1

The Great Monster Hunt

Norbert Landa

Tim Warnes

LITTLE TIGER PRESS
London

Early one morning, a funny noise woke up Duck.
It sounded like, pShh pShh! and it came from
right under her bed.

Duck was not quite sure what it was,
and she was much too afraid to look.

pShh pShh!

Instead, she jumped out of bed
and ran for help.

"Pig!" Duck yelled. "There is something under my bed and it's making strange sounds. It goes, pShh pShh, **grrr!**"

"Pshh pshh, **grrr**?" asked Pig. "Oh my! We need someone really strong to help. Stay right where you are!"

And Pig ran to find Bear.

Pig told Bear all about the frightening noise under Duck's bed. "It goes,

pshh pshh,

grrr,

bang bang!

I wanted to tell you, Bear, because you are so strong."

Bear lifted a huge log. "It is true I am strong enough for almost anything," he said. "But I think we'd better find someone who is *loud* enough to chase this thing away."

Bear told him the dreadful news about the terrifying thing under Duck's bed.

So they ran to find Wolf, who was about to start his early morning howling.

"It goes, pShh pShh,

grrr, bang bang,

wham wham —

all of the time!" Bear said.

"We thought you could help us frighten it away!"

"Oh yes, I can!" Wolf proudly said.

"There is no match for what

I can do. Just listen!

OOOOOOOO!

OWO

But maybe we also need help

from someone really clever."

So they ran to find Owl.

"Listen," Wolf said. "There is a dreadful and terrifying sound under Duck's bed. It goes, pShh pShh, grrr,

bang bang wham wham, grrrrowl!"

Owl was lost for words.

"We thought you might know what it was," Pig said, "because you are so clever!"

Owl said, "Clever, yes, that's what I am.
So I can tell you one thing:

Duck is in great danger!"

Pig, Bear, and Wolf huddled closer together.
"Are you sure?" they asked.

"Oh, yes," Owl said. "Can you imagine anything
kind and cuddly making such a noise?"

"It must be a monster!" yelled Pig.
"Oh, what are we going to do?"

"The only way to deal with
a monster," Owl said, "is to trap it."

Clever Owl!

So the animals set about gathering rope and nets
and useful pokey things. Then the four of them
bravely set off toward Duck's house.

Owl led the way, because trapping the monster was his clever idea. Next came Wolf, howling loudly. Then came Bear, with his monster-buster stick. Last was Pig, clutching his great monster-catcher net.

Finally they arrived at Duck's house
and flattened their ears against the door.
But no monstrous sound was heard— no
screaming nor crying nor calling for help.
  "Maybe we are too late?" whispered Bear.
  "Oh, nooo!" Pig cried in despair.
  "Duck, are you there?" called Wolf.

Then the door slowly creaked open . . .

It was Duck. "You're here!" she said.

"Duck! You are in great danger!" whispered Bear.

"There's a monster under your bed!" cried Pig.

Duck looked ready to faint.

"A monster?" she whimpered.

"How do you know?"

"Because it goes,

pshh pshh, grrr, bang bang, wham wham, grrrrowl!" Pig yelled.

"And, OOOOOOOOOeeeeee!" Owl added.

"Come on, let's get it!"
And the animals charged
into Duck's house.

Up the stairs they crept . . . then they heard a sound.

PShh pShh! it went.

It came from right under Duck's bed.

Owl flashed his lantern. The animals gasped.

They could not believe their eyes!

PShh PShh!

There, right under Duck's bed, was a tiny mouse,
snoring softly in its tiny bed, pshh pshh!

"Well I never!" Duck whispered.

"Do you know what we've just done?" Owl smiled.

All feeling rather silly, the animals looked at each
other and giggled . . .

"We've just made a **monster** out of a mouse!"

> *Maturity models are a recognized means by which organizations can measure their progress against established benchmarks. —AICPA/CICA Privacy Maturity Model*

The PMM uses five maturity levels:[2]

1. **Ad hoc.** Procedures or processes are generally informal, incomplete and inconsistently applied

2. **Repeatable.** Procedures or processes exist; however, they are not fully documented and do not cover all relevant aspects

3. **Defined.** Procedures and processes are fully documented and implemented and cover all relevant aspects

4. **Managed.** Reviews are conducted to assess the effectiveness of the controls in place

5. **Optimized.** Regular review and feedback are used to ensure continuous improvement towards optimization of the given process

Getting started with either example of maturity model, or even creating one of your own, can be done many ways. The AICPA/CICA PMM provides a structure to assist and identify where to start and what to document, as well as key start-up activities that include:[3]

- Identifying a project sponsor (chief privacy officer or equivalent)
- Appointing a project lead with sufficient privacy knowledge and authority to manage the project and assess the findings
- Forming an oversight committee that includes representatives from legal, human resources, risk management, internal audit, information technology and the privacy office
- Considering whether the committee requires outside privacy expertise
- Assembling a team to obtain and document information and perform the initial assessment of the maturity level
- Managing the project by providing status reports and the opportunity to meet and assess overall progress
- Providing a means to ensure that identifiable risk and compliance issues are appropriately escalated
- Ensuring the project sponsor and senior management are aware of all findings
- Identifying the desired maturity level by principle and/or for the entire organization for benchmarking purposes

These steps and many more can also be found in Chapter 2, Section 2.1, within the business case development steps. Accomplishing the maturity of the program provides the means to report the overall status for the return on investment (ROI) to the organization, as well as benchmarks to determine next steps to achieve a higher level of maturity. The privacy professional can use graphics, charts, written reports and other tools to benchmark the current status, while using those same tools to reflect improvements over time.

As the AICPA/CICA states, "In developing the PMM, it was recognized that each organization's personal information privacy practices may be at various levels, whether due to legislative requirements, corporate policies or the status of the organization's privacy initiatives. It was also recognized that, based on an organization's approach to risk, not all privacy initiatives would need to reach the highest level on the maturity model."[4]

An initial assessment can identify strengths and reveal weaknesses and gaps in your program. Areas needing attention might include deficiencies in technical controls or lack of training for employees; perhaps privacy requirements have not been fully integrated throughout all areas of the organization.

When a baseline assessment has been established, your organization can then decide at which level of maturity it ultimately wants or needs to operate. Not all organizations will need to operate at the highest level of maturity. Each organization should be intentional, though, in its commitment to increasing the maturity level of its privacy program.

1.2 Privacy by Design

Privacy by Design (PbD) is referenced in both Chapters 4 and 5 because the concept can be used to assess and/or protect, based on the needs of the organization. The privacy professional should assess the current organization objectives and goals to use PbD appropriately. PbD is a term developed by Dr. Ann Cavoukian, Information and Privacy Commissioner, Ontario, Canada, in the 1990s. PbD refers to the philosophy and approach of embedding privacy into the design of technology, business practices and physical design. Nymity is an ambassador for Privacy by Design focusing on business practices. Nymity created the privacy risk optimization process (PROP) to help organizations implement the philosophies of PbD into business practices.

The PbD framework dictates that privacy and data protection are embedded throughout the entire life cycle of technologies, from the early design stage to their deployment, use and ultimate disposal. The concept that organizations need to build privacy directly into technology, systems and practices at the design phase, thereby ensuring the existence of privacy from the outset, is the main principle.

1.2.1 Information and Privacy Commissioner, Ontario, Canada: Privacy by Design

"*Privacy by Design* (the Gold Standard for data protection), is *the* standard to be adopted for Smart Grid implementation for data protection. Embracing a positive–sum model whereby privacy and energy conservation may be achieved in unison is key to ensuring consumer confidence in electricity providers, as Smart Grid projects are initiated. Customer adoption and trust of Smart Grid energy savings programs is an integral factor in the success of energy conservation."[5]